Hindle

Bourton Founa.,

A Brief History of a

Country Engineering company.

David Eaton

Published by Holway Publications

ISBN 978 0 9555870 0 9

Introduction

Bourton in Dorset, on the old main A303 London to Exeter road, appears now to the casual visitor to be a typical small village with little to distinguish it from any other. However, in 1880, Kelly's directory notes that "here are an ironfoundry, boiler and agricultural implement manufacturer of some celebrity and extent, two manufacturers of flax and shoe thread, sack and sacking manufactory, a tannery, two brick and tile works, which give employment to a great number of hands, also two quarries yielding blue and sand stone suitable for building."

The Engineering works that became E.S. Hindley & Sons evolved from the blacksmiths shop that formed part of the earliest industrial development, the flax processing and spinning mill built by Daniel Maggs in about 1750.

The works reached its peak between 1890 and 1910. The First World War caused them to go over to war production, and a shortage of orders during the depression that followed prevented them from fully re-establishing peacetime production. The works closed in 1927, when the business and some of the staff were taken over by Dodmans of King's Lynn who continued to produce engines to the Hindley designs at their King's Lynn works.

Despite the wide variety of machinery produced, there is little surviving in preservation or museums today, and the firm is best represented by a number of catalogues that exist in various museums and private collections.

Chapter 1 Early development

The engineering business that became Hindley & Co. had its beginnings in a very different industry.

The area around Bourton, including parts of Somerset, Dorset and Wiltshire had been growing flax and processing the crop, involving retting, spinning and weaving, as a cottage industry since mediaeval times.

The Maggs family had lived in the area for many years, and became one of the principal landowners. In about 1750, Daniel Maggs built a factory powered by a waterwheel to perform all the processing of flax under one roof. This factory was on the site of what is now Bullpits house, where in the grounds, the long narrow retting ponds can still be seen. Later, another factory was built further downstream, and adjacent to the main road through the village, by William Jesse, who had married Rachel Maggs.

Jesse's mill expanded considerably over the next 40 years, with the introduction of a new material "linsey-woolsey", a heavy hard-wearing cloth with a linen warp and woolen weft. A rope-walk was also built.

By 1782, Jesse's mill, employed over 250 people, and a large blacksmiths shop has been built, power being supplied by an undershot water wheel in the river adjacent to Bourton Bridge. This mill had contracts with the Royal Dockyard, Plymouth for the supply of sail cloth.

Maggs mill had also expanded, and was now managed by Richard and Herbert Maggs. It seems likely that a new mill was constructed at this time, below the old mill buildings, to take advantage of the River Stour as a power source. Power was supplied by two waterwheels, and the availability of this enabled David Maggs (Daniel's son) to set up a small workshop to make harvesting and processing tools for flax workers, and also repairs and modifications to the mill machinery. This workshop also absorbed the smithy at Jesse's Mill, which closed in about 1801.

This branch of the works proved successful, and by 1810, Daniel, the son of David Maggs was also producing a small range of farm implements. At about this time, Daniel also made the first thrashing machine in the West of England, and a copy of his patent can be seen in Gillingham Museum.

In 1820, the Maggs' built a complete new mill on the same site, utilising all new machinery. This mill was described in a Parliamentary report of 1837 as being entirely water driven, having two waterwheels with a combined horsepower of 20, of which only 15 was used, and employing 68 people, 37 of them being between 13 and 18 years of age and four between 9 and 11.

Demands for power at the new mill led to the construction in 1837 of a additional breastshot waterwheel 60ft. (18.2m) in diameter, and 4ft (1.2m) wide. At the time, this was the largest waterwheel in England. (Some sources give a construction date for this wheel of 1832, but the date of the report above suggests that this is based on an error in transcription.) The retting ponds were altered to provide the water supply for this wheel. The penstock at the end of the old launder still exists.

The discovery of a bed of sand suitable for casting, in Breach Close, on the opposite side of the turnpike road, near the end of Mill lane, enabled Daniel Maggs to expand into ironfounding, and a cupola furnace was built. Coke and pig iron came from South Wales by ship to Bridgwater and thence by road.

Maggs engineering supplied many waterwheels to mills and factories, and some were used in Cornwall for mine pumping. A water wheel built by Daniel Maggs still exists at nearby Silton Mill.

The Hindley's were another local family. Henry Hindley who died in 1783 is described on his monument in Mere church as a merchant. His grandson Charles married Honour Maggs in 1817, the first mention of the Hindley name in connection with the mills at Bourton. In 1830, Samuel Hindley, Charles' brother, married Anne Maggs. Both Charles and Samuel are stated in the banns to be of St. Leonard's Shoreditch, although they were from a local family.

The need for linen sailcloth decreased with the introduction of cotton, and even more, later in the 19th. Century, with the use of steamships. This fall in spinning and weaving may have been a spur to the enlargement of the engineering side of the business which became Maggs & Hindley Engineering in 1821, the partners being Oliver Maggs and Henry Hindley, employing 140 workers in both the spinning and engineering businesses. Further enlargement of the works followed, and in 1838, a new foundry was constructed, and two waterwheels were in use to power the engineering works, the flax mill being driven solely by the 60 ft wheel.

Maggs and Hindley continued the production of waterwheels, some of those built by them including Park Farm at Stalbridge (1862), Melbury Abbas (1875), Stour Provost (1889) and West Mill Marnhull (1893). By the late 1830s

SMALL VERTICAL STEAM ENGINES,
With or without Boilers.
STATIONARY OR ON WHEELS.

Specially adapted to take the place of Horse Gears and Manual labour for all such work as Chaff-Cutting, Grinding, Pumping, Hoisting, &c. They have equilibrium, quick speed governors, turned fly-wheels, and feed-pump, and are very strong, simple, easily managed, economical in fuel, occupy the smallest space possible, and will work to twice their nominal power.

NOMINAL HORSE POWER.	1	1½	2	3	4	5	6	8	10
	£	£	£	£	£	£	£	£	£
Engine only	15	18	21	26	35	45	52	60	70
Engine and Boiler combined on Water-tank Foundation	39	47	55	70	88	100	115	135	157
Engine and Boiler on Three Wheels with handle	41	49	57	75	95	110	125	145	167
Engine and Boiler on Four Wheels, and horse shafts	42	50	59	79	97	112	128	150	172
Diameter of Cylinder	3 in	3½ in	4 in	5 in	5½ in	6½ in	7½ in		
Diameter of Fly-wheel	16 in	19 in	21 in	26 in	min	34 in	39 in		
Height of Boiler	3 ft	3½ ft	4 ft	3 ft	4½ ft	6 ft	6 ft 9		
Number of Vertical Tubes	7	7	12	12	12	18	18		

Ready for Delivery—A large number have been sold.

Catalogues, Terms, and Testimonials on application

they had introduced a range of "handy and efficient small motors for every domestic and other purpose in shops, dwellings and on farms to give drive to sewing and washing machines, turning lathes polishers and blowers, chaff cutters, butter churns, soda apparatus etcetera.".

They exhibited at agricultural shows all over the
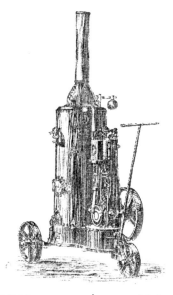
country, and their advertising extolled the virtues of steam engines over the horse, pointing out that the engine, unlike the horse, only required feeding when working, and could work longer hours that a horse. Equally valid were their cost comparisons, in that a two horsepower engine could be bought for the cost of one good horse.

Although other makers also entered this market, these little engines were the direct ancestors of the hordes of internal combustion "barn engines" made by all the major manufacturers later.

Chapter 2 Maggs & Hindley

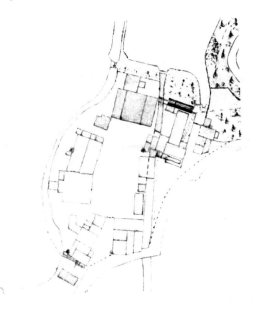

A plan dated 1857, in Dorset Records Office, which details the factory and Bullpits House, shows that by this time there were three waterwheels in use at what is described as a flax mill, foundry and grist mill. Also shown on this plan are the factory pond, the leats, and retting ponds all supplied with water by the River Stour. The estate at this time was owned by Oliver Maggs, most probably the son of Daniel. What influence Charles and Samuel Hindley had had on the development of the iron foundry is open to conjecture, but in the light of subsequent events it could have been considerable.

The 1859 edition of Kelly's Directory records " Oliver Maggs, agricultural implement maker, engineer, ironfounder and manufacturer of artificial manures". This is the only mention of artificial manures in connection with the various industries in Bourton, so it appears to have been only a short lived product

In 1861, Kelly's Directory describes the works as an "ironfoundry and agricultural implement manufactory of some celebrity and extent.", although the ownership is not stated. Oliver Maggs is listed as "flax spinner, shoe thread and sacking factory", so it appears the ironworks were a separate concern, almost certainly under the name of Maggs and Hindley.

By 1865, Kelly's directory entry records Edward S Hindley, engineer, millwright, ironfounder, agricultural implement manufacturer (late Maggs and Hindley), which appears to be a misprint for Edmund, while Uriah Maggs is recorded as "sack and sacking manufacturer, flax spinner, tow, jute and hemp spinner, and linen yarn manufacturer". Edmund, born in 1836, was the son of Charles Hindley.

The change in ownership may have been at least partially caused by the death of Charles or

Samuel Hindley, but as biographical data on these individuals is scarce, this can only be a speculation.

Edmund continued the production of the small steam engines, and introduced improvements to an already successful range. It appears that Edmund, or some one of his employees had a flair for design, which resulted in new items being produced, and the works production moving from mainly agricultural implements to more general engineering

By 1875,when catalogue No. 107 was issued, Hindley's had become known for the production of a range of small steam engines combined with boilers as a complete mobile

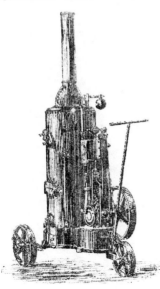

power unit for driving agricultural implements such as chaff cutters, feed mills etc. as a replacement for a horse mill.

The picture, dated 1876, shows one of the wheeled units, which were made in a range of sizes from 1 to 5 HP. Features of the design were that the cast iron base incorporated a water tank and the eccentric driving the valve also drove the feed pump. The boiler was made of best staffordshire iron. The engines were also available with the boiler but without wheels and as the engine alone.

Actual figures for the size of the factory and number of employees are difficult to obtain, as many of the quoted figures appear to include the workers at the flax mill. However the 1881 Census returns show that Edmund S. Hendly (sic) was living at Balpelts, Kings Green Cottage, with his wife Charlotte, five children, a governess and two domestic servants. Edmund is described as "Engineer employing 84 men and 22 boys."

This picture shows the factory at about 1900-1905.

At some time between 1885 and 1900, the flax mill closed, and the buildings were absorbed into the engineering works. At the same time the 60ft. waterwheel went out of use, and the entire factory was powered by steam. The picture shows what appears to be three boiler chimneys, and probably, steam escaping from a safety valve.

By the time that catalogue No.279 was issued, in 1905, the production of agricultural implements had been largely discontinued. Steam engines both vertical and horizontal were made, in sizes from 1 to 100 HP. All of the smaller engines were offered with a high-speed equilibrium governor, which appears to be of the "Hartnell" type. An optional extra was automatic expansion gear, which operated a cut-off valve. An interesting item from these lists is that in 1875, a 1 HP engine and boiler, mounted on wheels cost £41, and by 1905, the price had increased to £51.

During this period, the firm's products were exported worldwide. Many of their boilers were offered in variants suitable for wood firing, and a sectional boiler that could be easily carried across country was described in "The Engineer".

Chapter 3 Hindley & Sons.

Exactly when the change to Hindley and Sons occurred is unknown but it was by 1902, as a patent granted in that year is in the name of Edmund Samuel Hindley, Leonard Albert Hindley and Harold Douglas Hindley. This patent was connected with their newest product, steam wagons.

The first used a vertical boiler, with a compound engine 4½" and 7" bore by 6" stroke, mounted horizontally. This was extensively tested by being used for delivering coal to the factory from the station at Gillingham, carrying a load of

2 tons, with a trailer carrying 1½ tons. Several wagons of similar type were built and sold, but the vertical boiler used was found to be low on steam raising capacity for maximum power.

The subsequent wagons used the Hindley's design of stayless locomotive type boiler, with a compound engine with 3¾" and 7" bore 6" stroke cylinders. With a boiler pressure of 225 PSI, this would climb a gradient of 1 in 8 with a full load. 11 wagons of this pattern were sold to Messrs. Pickfords Ltd, as well as others to

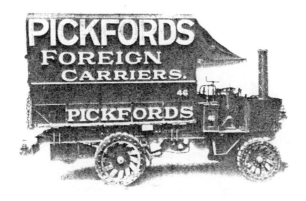

both local and national companies.

The well known problem of maintaining the water level over the firebox in this type of boiler when on a slope was avoided in this design by making the firebox higher, and the water level above the barrel. Firing was carried out from the top.

A variant of the wagon was made, called the Colonial. This had larger, wider wheels, a larger water tank, and an enlarged firebox for wood burning.

By this time, internal combustion engines had become more reliable and efficient, and in response to demand, Hindleys introduced their own design of gas engines in about 1906-1910. A design feature of these engines was the method adopted to avoid stresses in the cylinder casting.

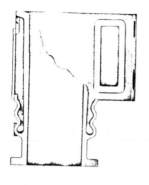

The water jacket portion of the casting was made with corrugations to allow for differences in expansion between inner and outer parts. These engines were offered with from 1 to 6 cylinders, and powers from 20 to 120 HP. It is not known how many of these engines were sold, but as a complete workshop was given over to their erection, it must have proved worthwhile.

This picture of about 1915, show part of the erecting shop for the gas engine range.

Catalogue 308, issued about 1912 gives details of the complete range of machinery produced, which is similar to the earlier 1905 range with the addition of steam wagons and gas engines, which are fully described in catalogue 330, issued at about the same time. The range now covers 12 to 225 HP at speed from 450 to 600 rpm.

By 1915, they had introduced a fully enclosed, high-speed vertical steam engine as shown below. Standing behind the engine is Arthur Fry, one of their engineers, who travelled all over the country for the firm. This picture was widely used in publicity material.

Production of these engines was, if not stopped, severely curtailed, by the First World War, when the factory went over to munitions production. The major items made were casing for Mills bombs, a type of hand grenade.

In 1917, production at the factory was badly disrupted by a flood caused when a dam at Stourton gave way after very heavy rain.

From the "Western Gazette" 4th.July 1917

Considerable damage of an extraordinary character was occasioned in the locality of Bourton, Gillingham, Wincanton & Stourton inn the early hours of Friday morning (June 29th 1917) as the result of a violent thunderstorm, accompanied by an unprecedented fall of rain, which broke over the locality on the previous afternoon and evening. Fortunately there was no loss of life, although several people had narrow escapes, but the material damage caused was of an exceptional character. It is impossible to give any estimate of financial loss, but a survey of the locality, which in many respects bears the appearance of a battle swept area rather than a peaceful countryside, makes it evident that many thousands of pound have been lost.

THE BURSTING OF THE LAKE

The cause of the great upheaval, so far as the valley of the Stour is concerned, was the breaking out of bound of a large sheet of water, known as the "new lake" on the estate of Sir Henry H. A. Hoare, Bart., of Stourton. This lake which is bounded on every side by woods, is 18 acres in extent, and lies in a narrow valley which runs in a southerly direction from Stourton. It receives the water which comes from the source of the River Stour, a spot some two miles distant, and also that of another stream, and normally it contains a huge quantity of water. At the southern end of the lake was a bridge over which passed the road to Gaspar, and under this bridge the waters of the Stour flowed from the lake on towards Bourton and Gillingham. The course of the stream is a very narrow one, the banks rising very steeply on either side, and the stream is confined to this narrow valley until Bourton is passed, when the river runs into more open country.

During the heavy weather of Thursday, the extraordinary quantity of between five and six inches of rain fell in this locality. This great increase of water had the effect of bursting the banks of the lake at its narrow outlet at Gaspar bridge, and the breach may also have been helped by the long spell of dry weather *experienced earlier. At any rate the irresistable pressure of this tremendous body of water carried everything before it. The bridge was entirely swept away, and the water having a free outlet, pushed on with alarming rapidity towards Bourton. The estate people living near the spot declared that the noise of the escaping water was like continuous thunder. The sweeping away of Gaspar Bridge left a great chasm some 30 feet deep from the roads on either side. Trees were uprooted and carried away downstream like so many straws.*

The great wave proceeded on its destructive course towards Bourton, and ran through and over the lake above the Bourton foundry. Here it apparently made a bed for itself, for it swept through the extensive workshops and caused damage of a most extraordinary character. Walls were thrown down, heavy machinery, including a steam lorry, was overturned and a large boiler was literally swept from one shop onto another. Many parts of the works were flooded to a depth of from five to ten feet. In the clerical department a large safe and its contents, estimated to weigh from 15cwt to a ton was overturned. Throughout the establishment there remains a deep layer of mud, and the machinery is entirely clogged with it. The caretaker was the only person on the premises at the time, fortunately or there may have been loss of life, so suddenly did destruction come. He made his escape from the house by means of the roof.

Among the more portable materials in and around the works there were some extraordinary disappearances. Some 200 to 300 tons of coal disappeared from the yard, and with the exception of occasional lumps scattered about the fields and gardens hundreds of yards away, there is no clue to its whereabouts – possibly it will be found later in the bed of the stream. Trolleys and heavy chests of metal were carried away, and some have been discovered stranded in fields or by the riverside long distances away. A heavy cart from the yard was found several hundred yards downstream resting on a small wooden bridge. With the exception of a portion of the land which stands on higher ground, the allotments with their crops at the southern end of the foundry were practically washed out of the ground.

It is recorded that for several years after the flood, Mills bomb cases were collected from the river as souvenirs

Production at the factory resumed after the clearance work was completed, and in 1918, the 60ft. waterwheel was dismantled for scrap, possibly used for munitions.

After the War, Hindleys returned to engine building, and also took on contracts for the production of small specialist units for the shipbuilding industry. The depression after the War rendered orders scarce, and several complaints were received from local residents about the noise from riveting operations in the boiler shop.

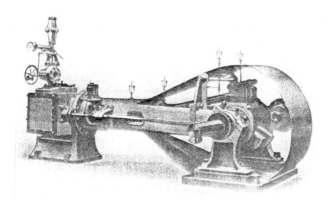

In March 1927, an article in "The Engineer" describes "an improved type of horizontal engine". Designed for export, it was intended to be intermediate in cost and efficiency between an ordinary steam engine, and a high-class engine with drop valves. The principal feature of the design was a "Y" shaped frame which was split and flanged so as to divide the engine into two main parts, the cylinder and crosshead unit, and the crankshaft unit. By the use of the "Y" frame, more rigidity was obtained than by an overhung crank, and the division simplified erection, which could be carried out without needing highly skilled labour. The two bearing pedestals of the crankshaft were dowelled and bolted to a cast iron soleplate, and had large flat faces to accept the feet of the "Y" frame. The crank unit is set in position, and levelled , and the cylinder unit can be bolted on and dowelled. This leaves the cylinder in the correct position, and can then be grouted in, thus avoiding alignment problems.

It would appear that this engine was not enough to restore the fortunes of the firm, and later in the same year, the firm was taken over by Dodmans of King's Lynn. The Hindley family, with some of the workforce also moved there.

Dodmans incorporated Hindley designs into their range. The "Dodman-Hindley" high speed vertical steam engine was notably successful, and some were still in use at Marham Pumping Station in 1976.

The factory at Bourton remained empty until 1933, when it was taken over by the Farma Cream Co. and converted to a milk processing and drying factory. During the Second World War, this was an important source of dried and powdered milk. The company was taken over by Unigate Dairies, and remained in use until the late 1980s.

Despite the number of engines and other machines produced during the existence of the company, very few items survive in preservation.

A few of the dozens of waterwheels still exist, there are a couple of steam engines in museums, and a portable engine exists in Australia, where it is displayed at steam rallies.

Appendix 1

The workforce employed by the mills, ironfoundry and other industries was considerable. The North Dorset Traction Company obtained an Act of Parliament in 1874 for the construction of a light railway between Bourton and the neighbouring village of Zeals across the county border. Work on this started in 1876, and the line was formally opened on 15th August 1877 by the local MP, Sir Frederick Whitmarsh. Services on the line were provided by a steam railcar built by the Bourton foundry. At peak times, this was augmented by a covered open sided wagon hitched on.

The line ran from Bell's lane Zeals to a point just beyond the Red Lion (now closed) in Bourton, with two intermediate stops. It appears that it was not very profitable, and by 1883, services had been stopped. The track was lifted in 1891, and sold to the Lynton & Barnstaple Railway. No trace of this undertaking now survives, and the only record is a pencil sketch by A. R. Moyt, RA. This shows two children, and behind them the railcar, and behind it, the High St factory. (Originally the Jesse mill, it is now part of Bourton Fencing)

Appendix 2

Sources and Acknowledgements

i)   King's Lynn Museum
ii)   Gillingham museum
ii)   Gillingham Public Library
iv)   Rural Life Museum, Reading.
v)   Phoenix Publications
vi)   Mere Museum
vii) Dorchester Public Library
viii) Dorchester Records Office

I acknowledge with gratitude the assistance of the staff of all the places named above in the research into the company which is the subject of this monograph.